CW00735371

TO ALL

THE NEW PARENTS

WE HAVE MET AND WORKED

WITH FOR BECOMING

CATALYSTS FOR THIS

BOOK PROJECT

BREASTFEEDING
for dads

THE GUIDE FOR TRULY HANDS-ON FATHERS

By Dr Russ King and Claudia A. Pfeiffer

The information in this book is aimed at maintaining general health and well-being. There are always limits to the benefits of self-treatment. As we stress in the book, medical specialists like a doctor or midwife should be consulted in the case of serious illness, or for any persistent symptoms.

The publisher and authors are not responsible for any specific health or allergy need that may require medical supervision and are not liable for any damages, or negative consequences from any treatment, action, application or preparation, to any person reading or following the information in this book.

All rights reserved. No part of this book can be reproduced or stored in a photo-mechanical or electronic form without the permission of the publisher.

© Smiling Cat Publishing GmbH,
Lenaustr. 1, 66125 Saarbrücken, Germany

ISBN 978-3-9444112-2-4
Illustrations, layout & typesetting: Bettina Weyland
Editorial and proof-reading: Victoria Johnston, Sophie Wölbling

NEW DAD GUIDE

Isn't parenting mostly instinct? It's happened for endless generations before you.

It's the oldest story in the world. Boy meets girl. Boy manages to seduce girl, or – if he is really lucky – girl seduces boy. They have some fun together and then one special night (or it could be a lunch break – there's no judgement here) sperm meets egg and a new life is created.

Everything seems so warm and fuzzy, like a feel-good Disney film. Perhaps that's a bad analogy – have you noticed how quickly parents tend to get killed off in those films? The truth is that a new baby sparks a massive change for the parents and much of this is very one-sided. The man's baby-creating role is brief (hopefully not too brief) but the woman nurtures the baby in her body for nine months and then feeds it after the birth.

Not all new mums are able to produce breast milk to order and there are a number of reasons for this. One of the main issues is that the breastfeeding mechanism is very sensitive to stress. Many women feel as if they have completely failed as a Mum if their new arrival is not immediately breastfeeding. This can increase stress levels and create a negative spiral.

But what can a father do when Mum has all the in-built gadgets?

It's time to learn some 'soft' skills: studies have shown that the breastfeeding process is more likely to be successful if the father provides a supportive role. It's not all going to be easy, but it's a lot less painful than squeezing the equivalent of a rugby ball out of your backside!

Luckily parts of this supportive role are quite obvious. Most fathers offer sympathy and support during pregnancy for bouts of morning sickness, cravings or emotional mood swings. Offering massages and always finding your partner gorgeous will also help. Imitating the warning signal of a reversing lorry when she is moving backwards – not so much!

However, doing the right things at the right times after the birth becomes an important skill to help minimise the negative effects of stress.

The core objective of this book is to give you the tools and methods you need to be a calm, reassuring influence on the teambuilding process. While men cannot breastfeed a baby, they can work behind the scenes to massively improve the experience for Mum and baby and help bond the new family.

The last thing we want is for you to start running around the house shouting "Don't panic! Keep calm or your milk will fail!" when the going gets tough.

Vilfredo Pareto was a 19th century economist who noticed that 80% of the land in Italy was owned by 20% of the population. This 80/20 rule, or Pareto principle, has since been applied to a myriad of different situations.

For example, we know that 80% of sales of this book will come from activities that take only 20% of our marketing time. Did you know that 20% of beer drinkers drink 80% of the beer drunk in the world? Or that we wear 20% of our clothes 80% of the time? There will be lots of extra clothes washing to do when the baby arrives but you're bound to use only 20% of the available cycles on your washing machine 80% of the time. It's not an exact science but many of life's activities break down into roughly 80/20 proportions.

Many fathers feel sidelined when a baby arrives but their actions often take place in that important 20% of time. The good news is that this 20% of time can be predicted again and again.

We want to encourage you to ensure your daddy time makes your new family life easier and more rewarding for everyone.

We are not claiming your 20% is going to eclipse your partner's effort! However, your actions can have a massive impact on bringing your new family together. Whatever your success rate you will definitely be one up on Vilfredo Pareto.

The male and female brain are wired differently, especially when it comes to communication. Women 'think aloud' a lot more than men and tend to speak more words in a day. They are also more likely to share their day-to-day experiences. Problems can sometimes arise when people (it's not always men, some women do this too)

see this sharing process as a specific request to solve particular problems.

Take this example from an expectant couple with an imminent due date who are sitting down to dinner after a day at work.

Woman: I can't believe there was a frost this morning. It's been so warm recently. The ice was so thick on the car windscreen. It took me ages to clear it off. I was so cold!

Man: Why didn't you use the de-icer spray I bought you?

Woman: (Angrily) I took it out of the car the other week. It's been so warm I didn't think I would need it.

Man: We're still likely to get frosts for a few weeks yet. It's still early in the year.

Woman: (Sends dagger glares down the table)

Man: What? It's way too early for the frosts to stop!

She already knows she made a mistake in taking the de-icer spray out of the car too early. She just wants to share her frustrating experience.

He was thinking of his pregnant wife stretching over the bonnet to scrape her windscreen. He only wants to stop her being in discomfort again. However, if he took a step back, he would have realised she is intelligent enough to work out her mistake.

It could have gone much better if it had gone more like this:

Woman: I can't believe there was a frost this morning. It's been so warm recently. The ice was so bad on the car windscreen. It took me ages to clear it off. I was so cold!

Man: Nightmare! It was freezing wasn't it? Did it take you long to warm up?

Woman: Ages! You know how long it takes for my car heater to get going. I was still cold when I got to the office and then the baby started kicking like mad in my first meeting!

Man: It's going to be a footballer! Have you run out of de-icer?

Woman: No. I stupidly took the de-icer out of the car the other week as it has been so warm.

Man: Poxy weather!

Extra bonus points if he checked the weather forecast for the next morning and made time to clear the ice off her windscreen before he left for work.

This is an extreme example and runs the risk of being described as 'mansplaining' itself! However, we are using it to demonstrate how we can empathise when it matters (in this case listening without criticism) and take proactive steps to improve the situation (clearing the ice off the windscreen for her).

By taking a relatively small amount of time out of his day our fictional man is able to remove significant discomfort for his partner. It will also give her that warm glow you get when someone does something nice for you without being asked. Warm glows reduce stress. We like warm glows!

A new baby instantly becomes everyone's main focus. It will be noisy, demanding and exhausting. The new parents are often overlooked. Your partner will feel that warm glow even more when you think ahead and do simple tasks for her. She may be the only one who can actually feed the baby, but it really helps to know she is not alone and that she has your loving support.

The father's **IMPORTANT** role in breastfeeding

Let's get the smutty giggles out of the way right now. Many men are obsessed with breasts. Adverts for men blatantly, and presumably successfully, use images of women with alluring breasts. It can be argued that some female celebrities owe their fame to the content of their bras – even more so if they're famous for not wearing them.

Breasts may be an important part of sexual attraction but their primary function is to produce milk for the baby. You may feel very attached to your partner's breasts but you've got company now. Hopefully your baby is going to spend a lot of time physically attached to them.

Unfortunately, Mum and baby may not take to it as easily as your eyes are drawn to a prominent cleavage. Breastfeeding creates a wonderful bond between mother and child, as well as providing many health benefits for Mum and the baby in later life. However, it can often create difficulties, frustrations and embarrassments. And this is where you come in! Your partner's breasts won't be your personal playthings for a while, but you can still be very hands-on in other ways.

It will be your role to think ahead and make life easier for Mum, to keep stress levels down. It is also just as important to develop a strong bond between you and your new baby.

One useful analogy is the onboarding approach used by budget airlines. The plane is prioritised and everything falls into place behind that. The customers are treated like sheep: they are herded to the boarding gates early and left to wait to board the plane. This prevents any delays in getting the passengers on board, thus helping the service to run on time, or maybe to squeeze another flight into the daily schedule.

The baby is always the priority, but you make Mum and yourself your second priority. All the other people are passengers. They are very welcome but they have to wait their turn.

If you are organised enough to be reading this before the birth you can start using our 'Breastfeeding for dads' principles now.

Some surprisingly useful tasks include:

- Keeping away those mums who insist on recounting every last grisly detail of their painful childbirth experiences to pregnant women!

- Helping to get the 'nest' ready, decorating the nursery and assisting with anything that prepares you both for the new arrival.

- Taking on any tasks, such as grocery shopping, that would keep your partner on her feet when she's heavily pregnant.

- Massage. There are lots of tips for this later in the book.

- Organising family members who want to buy key items for the new baby to avoid duplication (and to guide them into buying things you both actually want).

You can also work with your partner to decide what to include in the birth plan. For example, if you both decide you want there to be skin-to-skin contact between mother and baby this can be written down so the midwife and other professionals know about your wishes. The birth staff will be anxious to do their best to correspond to your wishes – while allowing for everything to be done in the 'X-Factor Baby's' best interests.

However, your biggest (and continuous) task is to get ready for fatherhood – to be(come) the dad you want to be. It is thought that a father's role is heavily influenced by their perception of their own fathers or grandfathers. Roles change over time but some families feel that the birth and the ensuing care for a new baby is very much female territory where men should take a back seat. Is this the role you want to play? It's your baby and your choice – along with your partner. Now is the time to discuss these roles and make a plan for after the baby is born. It is very likely this plan will be adjusted around the reality of life with your newborn, but it helps to have established the roles you would both like to play.

BEING HELPFUL DURING THE BIRTH PROCESS

The female reproductive cycle is far from user-friendly. Women can experience days of pain and discomfort every month for about 40 years to be able to have a few children. The process of childbirth has also not been designed from the mother's perspective. Humans have evolved into the dominant species on earth by developing large brains and having an extended childhood. This allows us to learn essential skills during teenage years like earning maximum likes on an Instagram selfie or winning the World Cup on FIFA.

Joking aside, there are three main theories on why human babies are born at their specific size and state of development:

1. Women have reached the maximum pelvis size that will allow the baby's head to pass through during the birth, without restricting the woman's efficiency and speed of movement as she lives her life. This is complicated by our upright stance compared to other higher primates.

2. The baby is born at the point where its consumption of energy and nutrients from the mother reaches a critical point. If she was to carry the baby for longer her health would start to be compromised.

3. Once the baby is born its rate of growth and development slows to match the reduced levels of energy provided by breast milk, compared to the umbilical cord.

Babies are born early in their development because humans are such social animals and they need time to pick up the culture and nuances of the humans around them.

Whichever way you look at it babies are born with large heads that need to emerge into the world through a small exit. We've all seen birth scenes in films where the mother is raging and screaming, often at the helpless-looking father who's not sure if he wants to hold her hand or faint.

Having a baby is exhausting: it's a bit like running a marathon as the waves of contractions go on and on. You might notice in those movie birth scenes that the midwives give even more encouragement just as the baby is almost in sight. This is not because they are looking forward to a coffee break! It's because this is when the woman is at her lowest ebb, when she'd really like to just have a rest and come back later to have another go.

The birth is everything; it's a sacred moment. It might feel that time stands still. The baby's environment completely changes and you and your partner are re-born as Mum and Dad. Most men would prefer to take the pain and discomfort during labour themselves rather than watching someone they love go through it. Others are secretly very pleased they avoid it!

The good news is that the female body is flooded with hormones during the birth process. In effect she is in a kind of birth bubble and this helps her cope with some of the pain and discomfort. It also helps that women are much tougher than they look! It's important to remember this during the birth process.

Work out together how you might be of help during the birth and be prepared to improvise. Do everything you can to support her, but think of yourself too. Childbirth can be very quick or it can take days. Don't just make sure your partner has all the refreshment she needs; take some time to feed yourself. You will be no help if you are spent after the birth when you actually did very little other than worry and stress.

Do you remember that birth plan? That wish you both had for quick skin-to-skin contact? Your partner may be too tired to ask for this if the midwife forgets about it. Or maybe the birth process was slightly different to the way that was planned – your baby is the star of the show and they can decide to do things their way! You can keep track of this and liaise between Mum and the professionals so your wishes as parents are understood.

Of course, not all births occur in the intended location. Sometimes the little cherubs arrive really quickly! Make sure you know all about the birth process and what you could be doing to help. You could end up helping to deliver your baby in the back of a car!

Having said this, you do have the option to define your role as a birth companion and this can include not being present at the birth if you do not want to be. This is something you need to talk about with your partner and agree in advance. If this is the case another birth companion should be arranged, such as a best friend or a doula.

The baby has arrived and everyone is relieved, excited and a bit overwhelmed. If the baby arrived in the hospital, or in a planned birth at home, there should be a midwife to look after Mum's immediate needs and to help start breastfeeding. Their knowledge is invaluable as they have helped a great many new mothers and their babies successfully start the process. While a baby often takes to breastfeeding like a fish to water, Mum can sometimes be hesitant to dip her toe into the water. She can miss a breastfeeding role model, even when the advice can be as simple as trusting her gut feelings and intuition.

It might seem strange that something as natural as breastfeeding might not come naturally. However, the whole birthing process brings the inside to the outside and leaves the new mum in a hurt and opened state. She needs to find cover – a shield to deflect extra opinions from the outside – as every intervention and bout of active thinking can slow down hormones and thus the process of breastfeeding. She needs to stay in the zone of being a new mum to let the natural process run its course.

Mum is usually kept in the hospital overnight, so your first role outside of your new inner family circle is to relay news to family and friends. If you're posting photos on social media make sure you agree which photos to post, considering they will probably be seen by people you both hardly know.

You should also be in charge of controlling visitors. If it's been agreed that family and close friends see the baby as soon as possible, it's your job to make that happen. If you both wanted a bit of peace before the surge of visitors, it's your job to enforce that.

Get home and get some sleep once the excitement is over. Don't go out 'wetting the baby's head' with your friends. A hangover has no place in the first few days after birth!

When you return home as a family the attention will instantly shift away from the new mum. She may have been a minor celebrity when she was pregnant but your new baby will steal all the limelight – an instant A-list celebrity! You will not only have lots of house visitors; your everyday tasks like grocery shopping will be interrupted by strangers cooing over your baby.

Your amazing partner grew and nurtured your new family member inside her and has given birth to this wonderful new little human. While the paparazzi shine their focus on the new arrival, your main role is to protect and nurture Mum. It might help to picture yourself wearing sunglasses (while it's dark) and a cheap suit. You are the bouncer, the doorman, the gatekeeper. If their name's not down, they're not coming in!

The good news is that the paparazzi will consist of your family and friends (unless you are a celebrity). Unfortunately, this can also be the bad news! These people can be the most difficult to keep at arm's length when Mum needs some peace. Especially if they think they are helping. Your task is to ensure these offers of assistance are channelled into ways that actually help your new family unit, as well as giving the visitors the baby interactions they crave. We will cover this later in the book.

You will receive lots of 'good advice'. Some of this will conflict with the way you have decided to raise your baby. We will discuss this later, but you can inject some fun into the situation for the two of you by creating a 'bullshit bingo' for the common phrases and suggestions you receive!

You can bet that someone will say something along the lines of "You can just sit and look at her for hours, can't you?" This is often said just as you're thinking of all the things you need to get done.

However, we have got ahead of ourselves, so let's take a step back and consider just why breastfeeding is so important.

THE BENEFITS
of breastfeeding

"The mothers may rest, to nurse their children themselves, so the customs will improve by themselves, and the impulses of nature will grow up again in all hearts."

Jean-Jacques Rousseau

The earlier the newborn is placed on the breast, the better the baby bonds. This makes it easier for mother and child to become a well-rehearsed breastfeeding team.

With your help, this becomes a well-rehearsed team of three laying the foundation for a wonderful and harmonious breastfeeding family relationship. There are many tips to try in this book if and when this fine balance breaks or falters.

Breastfeeding goes far beyond the intake of food: it is physical and emotional feeding, creating intimate contact between mother and child and giving the infant not only security and support, but also nest protection, allergy prevention and immunity through antibodies in breast milk.

Breast milk contains everything a baby needs for optimal physical and mental development: including fats, proteins, carbohydrates, vitamins, minerals and antibodies. It is perfectly adapted to the baby's needs at all times. Even the proteins are optimally tuned for the development of the small human baby.

Although the World Health Organisation recommends a breastfeeding period of up to two years, infants are often weaned after only four months or the diet is quickly changed to bottle-fed formula feeding and supplementary food. There will be many factors in deciding how long to breastfeed a baby.

This book is aimed at helping mums to start breastfeeding and then to find a rhythm to help them continue for as long as it benefits both Mum and baby. The first breast milk the baby receives is the most important. It can lay a good foundation for the child's life.

This in itself can put huge pressure on the new mum. If she is not able to breastfeed, for whatever reason, you should not harass her by insisting she continues to try for the sake of the health of her baby.

The new
LOVE TRIANGLE

Love triangles are usually bad news for someone. It could be two potential suitors fighting for the one soulmate, or infidelity bringing a third party into a relationship. Love triangles rarely have equal sides; they tend to be tall with a sharp point. No doubt you've guessed who tends to be the smaller side when it comes to the 'baby honeymoon' stage! Statistics show that dads who feel helpless, or who are reduced to being a 'service provider', spend more time away from their new family, often putting more hours into work.

So how do you equalise the triangle to include the needs of everyone?

You need to talk – both the easiest and hardest task! In this baby honeymoon it is important to discuss, define and plan your new roles so you can adjust and get used to each other with your new family. The sooner you do this, the easier it will be for you to integrate with your new family unit of three.

A NEW TAKE ON QUALITY TIME

It's important to work out what your time as a couple could look like and when it could happen. How can tasks be distributed and when can you sit down together? For example, most people wouldn't want to be handed a grumpy baby the moment they walk in the door after a day at work. Just being given ten minutes to get changed and empty your head of work can make a huge difference, even if your partner really needs a break! You need to be aware that you are both tired at the end of a 'working' day and manage the sharing of childcare so it works for both parties.

The most basic of tasks can be handled in different ways. Take getting up in the morning, for example.

You could:

- Creep out of the bedroom in the morning leaving the other two sides of the triangle to catch up on sleep.

- Bring your partner breakfast in bed so she can do the morning feed with minimal effort.

- Get up a bit earlier before work to be in charge of your baby so your partner can grab a shower after a broken night's sleep.

- Both avoid a morning shower and have cuddle in the bath in the evening when the baby is sleeping.

Of course, rules are made to be broken. You could walk into the house after work, put the baby in his pram and go out for a walk. This can clear your head while spending time with your new arrival. It gives your partner a breather at the same time. Of course, it doesn't end when you find a routine that works as you will continuously have to adapt as the baby develops.

We're all different, so discuss what could work for you both and prepare to change or improve your tactics! Remember that time shared with your partner when you are both 'present' is really important. Collapsing in front of the TV doesn't really count unless you are cuddled up and have not drifted off into a zombie state! Multi-tasking is allowed to an extent such as cuddling and calmly discussing your days while Mum is breastfeeding.

Another tactic that focuses on maintaining the bond between you and your partner is to have a fixed day every month where you spend time together. An example would be a date night. This could start during pregnancy so you develop a routine. When the baby arrives you'll need a babysitter and you may not want to dress up, or go very far or for very long. You will probably both appreciate the chance to take a break together. This may not work for all couples due to difficulties with expressing milk or finding a babysitter you trust. One solution is to start a mutual babysitting circle with other parents from your antenatal classes or friends who have recently had a baby.

DADS NEED 'ME TIME' TOO!

Just because you've become a dad doesn't mean that you have to be one 24/7. Yes, it's good to take the baby out for a walk but you might really need to burn off some steam. Go for a run, have a kick about with friends. You don't have to give up all your hobbies. You will find that life calms down as the new baby grows and your family finds a routine. You need time to yourself in the same way that Mum needs an occasional break from being the primary carer. It just needs to be more carefully planned than before the baby arrived.

Sex was the glue between you when you first got together, the thrill that sparked the excitement of the new relationship. Then you got your partner pregnant and your sex life changed. You may not have had sex for some time and may feel as randy as a rabbit, or your libido might have plummeted. Either way it is unlikely your partner is going to feel mischievous in bed for a while. This transition period depends on any physical or emotional damage, her (and your) sleep levels, how she views her body after the pregnancy and childbirth and getting used to her new role as a mother.

All of this is understandable but you are both going without an important way of reaffirming the bond between you. There may not be lust between you at the moment, but don't forget the importance of a tender kiss and reminding her that you still fancy the pants off her. This will help rekindle the sensual bond between you that will in due course resume into an active sex life.

Don't let sex become a taboo subject. Talk about it, reassure each other that your physical connection is still there even if it is not at the top of your mind at the moment. Just remember to talk about contraception before getting active again!

TEAMBUILDING
for the young family

'It takes a village to raise a child.'

Nigerian proverb

We've discussed how the babymoon love triangle is important but this doesn't mean you should close yourselves off. Your three-person triangle can become a whole village with family members and friends taking on some of the new tasks, while specialists like health visitors and midwives provide expert support. It is a whole new symbiosis.

Make use of these people if you have concerns about anything, including any problems your partner is having in adapting to her new role. You might also want to get into the habit of getting a trusted and experienced person to babysit on a regular basis for you.

If you don't have family or friends you can lean on, there is also the option of hiring a doula – a non-medical advisor who can help with breastfeeding and care of newborn babies.

Of course, you don't want a whole village to turn up at your house all carrying a home-cooked lasagne (if three wise women had attended the birth of Jesus at least one of them would have brought a lasagne) and wanting to cuddle the new arrival.

While breastfeeding is a completely natural thing to do, it does raise some potential embarrassment issues. Whilst the process can be very discreet with practice, a new mum may not want to be going through her learning stages in front of specific people. There may also be visitors who feel uncomfortable with the potential of mum's breast being visible. The temptation is to tell them to get over themselves, but their uncomfortable behaviour can create awkwardness. There may also be some people she would rather not expose herself to for whatever reason. You can solve these issues by finding a different task for these visitors at key times so they feel they are helping.

It's your job to navigate the way through any potential stressful situations for Mum and we'll explain exactly how and why in the following sections. As a partner, you are the key support when it comes to breastfeeding: the more normal and natural you are about the breastfeeding process, the easier it will be for your partner.

This attitude can make the small but subtle difference in the big decision of whether your child is breastfed or bottle-fed from an early age. A negative attitude from you can threaten the future breastfeeding relationship between mother and child. It can lead to a lack of milk production or the 'drying up' of milk after a short time. The new mother is very sensitised by the strenuous birth and the resulting maelstrom of hormones and can react badly to what feels like rejection.

There are even men who are afraid of what the breastfeeding process will do for the physical appearance of their partner's breasts, or who feel jealous because the baby now gets more attention. Don't be one of these men!

In short, it's important that neither of you feel excluded. You are still the couple you were before. You now have a different focus, but it can bring you even closer together. If you do start to feel excluded you need to share these feelings. She'll probably surprise you by saying something along the lines of: "I feel excluded too.

Sometimes it feels like I am on my own with the baby".

You might wonder how she can feel excluded when she's the one with the baby that everyone wants to see. This feeling is often caused by the endless small decisions that have to be made when looking after a baby. It really helps to share them with someone. If you can discuss how many of these decisions you can make together, or which responsibilities you can take on, you are creating a fabulous new family unit.

Remember when we warned you about mansplaining? This is your time to shine as you will choose to only offer advice when it is requested. Unfortunately you'll both get loads of unwanted advice from people – especially when you really just want to get some sympathy. If you admit how tired you are because the baby doesn't sleep at night, you can expect a selection of these, sometimes all in one conversation:

- "Have you been burping him enough?"

- "You need to give him a bath just before bed."

- "Have you been giving her enough stimulation?"

- "Have you been giving her too much stimulation?"

- "Have you tried ignoring him? He'll soon give up."

- "Have you tried letting her sleep in your bed?"

- "She's not sleeping in your bed, is she? That causes no end of problems!"

Your role as a breastfeeding dad is to gently deflect any unwanted advice and change the subject.

While your partner is breastfeeding to nourish your baby's needs, you can nourish the baby's soul through your being there, your attentive presence and caring for your little family.

The American pediatrician Dr William Sears, who is also Associate Clinical Professor of Pediatrics at the University of California, Irvine, School of Medicine, and his wife Martha, nurse and breastfeeding consultant, have shaped the educational philosophy of attachment parenting. In a nutshell, he sees 10 rules that could apply to breastfeeding mothers and equally their partners.

This may not work for everyone, but the general idea is the same as our low-cost airlines analogy. Your partner and baby are the priority: everything else has to go through security!

The Sears' 10 rules of postpartum

1. You shouldn't cook, clean the house, do laundry or entertain guests.

2. You shall take a doula.

3. You should wear your bathrobe during the day and stay in the rocking chair as long as you like.

4. You shall honour your partner by letting him do his part of the housework.

5. You shall not have your baby looked after by strangers.

6. You shall take walks in beautiful woods or on green meadows, eat well and drink enough.

7. You shall not let any strange or annoying guests into your house.

8. You shall have an easy-care, pretty hairstyle and let your body be pampered with soothing care products.

9. You should not surround yourself with people who are not helpful to you with advice around the baby.

10. Sleep when your baby is asleep.

10 WAYS of being the PERFECT PAIR

Perfection is achieved, not when there is nothing more to add, but when there is nothing left to take away.

Antoine de Saint-Exupéry

It's time to discuss the really important stuff – how you can help with breastfeeding. It's time to man up and show up. Remember, we are following the 80/20 rule here, so your role is not all-consuming. It's more about the little things you can do to make Mum feel more relaxed and to create a strong new family unit. Breastfeeding is a full-time job, especially in the first days after the marathon of childbirth.

1. It's no surprise that breastfeeding makes your partner thirsty, so simply bringing her a glass of water can be a huge help. Especially if the little cherub has decided it is time for a really long, sleepy feed. It can be hugely frustrating to be craving something as simple as a drink but not be able to get it. It's even worse if there is a glass of water in the room but you can't reach it.

2. You've probably already guessed this too, but a snack is often well received when the baby is being refueled. This can be anything that contributes to a well-balanced diet (bearing in mind that an interesting balanced diet involves treats too!). There are a selection of snacks that are beneficial to both Mum and the baby in our recipe section later in the book.

3. Now you've got a well-fed and watered mum, but she's got nothing to do! This is not a big issue if your baby feeds like a barracuda with quick, short feeds, but it can be if your baby feeds slowly like a sleepy lamb. Make sure she is not stranded out of reach of entertainment. One tactic is to have a little box of useful things that can be placed near Mum when she is breastfeeding. This could contain things like a book (that is not too heavy to read one handed!) or an e-reader, or access to an audiobook, snacks, a bottle of water, a flannel, a toy for an older sibling, or maybe the TV remote if watching television is not too distracting. Ask her what she would like!

4. The phone. This subject is nearly as contentious as whether pineapple is an acceptable pizza topping! A good rule of thumb is that phone calls can wait until after the feeding session. Switching to airplane mode or muting the phone are good tactics, especially in the first few days of breastfeeding. The rest of the world will wait until the baby has been burped and is settled. Once breastfeeding routines are really established it might be enjoyable for Mum to flick through social media or play on some apps. Some mums will be able to chat with certain friends on the phone but this should be relaxing for Mum and not distracting for the baby. We all have 'drainer' friends who take more than they give and 'radiator' friends who give us a boost. If this sort of distraction works for your partner make sure you know who she wants to talk to.

5. Playing good cop/bad cop is an essential role for the breastfeeding dad. If a 'drainer' is causing trouble it's your job to sort it, even if they happen to be a key family member or close friend. You can discuss it with your partner but if there's an awkward conversation to be had, you will be the person doing it. If they are on the phone, telling them she is changing a spectacularly messy nappy should do the trick!

6. Preventing isolation – it's one thing to be cocooned against all negative influences, quite another to feel trapped and isolated. Mum needs more than just her magical bond with the new baby. Now is the time to forge the strong bonds of your new family unit. Don't busy yourself doing other tasks if you've got the opportunity to spend some extra time with them both.

7. She may also feel insecure about herself. She might also worry that she is not going to be a good enough mum. After all, it's not really something you can practice in advance. She might also have concerns about her body. Once upon a time she relished the sexual attraction you had for her. Since then her stomach ballooned and now a key part of her feminine allure has transformed into a double-barrelled feeding device. Let her know that you love her and encourage all the good things she is doing. Make sure you face any fears or problems together, try to laugh at mistakes (we've all made them) and celebrate your successes.

8. Take your turn in feeding the baby. No, we're not expecting you to produce the milk yourself, but once your partner has grown used to breastfeeding she may be able to express milk. This means you can take a pre-dawn shift or maybe just be left with the baby by yourself for a longer period of time so Mum can snatch a quick break if she wants to.

9. While it's natural to want to get the hang of breastfeeding at home your partner will also need to feed the baby while out and about. Breastfeeding is a perfectly natural process but it could help for you to be with her during her first experiences of breastfeeding out of the house, at least until she has confidence in this new activity in the public arena.

10. Celebrate successes and commiserate with difficulties. There will be times when the baby will do exactly as she is programmed to do and feed without fuss or drama. There will also be 'other' times! By being involved in both good and bad you will also be learning how to soothe and comfort your baby when she is handed over to you.

The
SCIENCE behind
BREASTFEEDING

When you buy a new car you get a huge user manual, but the process of actually driving the car is more straightforward than ever. Most people will spend more time reading how to use the sat nav or how to connect their phone to the car than finding out how to actually drive it.

Breastfeeding should be as simple. Have baby, put baby on nipple, baby drinks milk, baby needs winding and then baby goes to sleep. Of course, it is not always this simple, so here is a look beneath the bonnet (or bra) so you can understand why your role is so important.

THE BREAST GROWS WITH ITS TASKS

You may already find breasts fascinating, but the fact that their specialised tasks lie dormant until a baby is born is worth further exploration. Not only do they produce milk after the birth of the child, they provide the optimum ingredients at the right time. The milk just after birth is different to that produced a few weeks after birth. If the baby is premature the milk content is perfectly suited to a premature baby's needs.

You would think that with this ridiculously sophisticated 'technology' the breastfeeding process would not be so sensitive to the stressful demands of modern life!

Anyway, back to the science. The production of milk is stimulated by the hormone prolactin but this is also kept in check by the hormone HPL (human placenta lactogen – this is produced in the placenta), oestrogen, progesterone and dopamine until after the baby and placenta is born.

BREAST MILK – A VERY SPECIAL JUICE

Mother's milk is much more than just food for your baby.

Research shows that breastfeeding can lay a valuable foundation and counteract many metabolic diseases by passing on antibodies and microbes from the mother. This can also include resistance to allergies. The World Health Organisation states that 'Breastfed children perform better on intelligence tests, are less likely to be overweight or obese and less prone to diabetes later in life.' One reason for the improved brain development could be the composition of human milk compared to formula that is made from cow, goat or sheep milk. The milk from these animals has a higher protein content as their priority is to develop muscles to help them escape predators.

It should be noted that recent studies have shown a less clear-cut result for an increase in intelligence with breastfeeding when other factors like the education or income levels of the mother are examined. Mothers who are well-educated and in higher income brackets are more likely to breastfeed than mothers with lower levels of education and lower incomes.

Some scientists claim that allergies, diabetes or obesity can be triggered by colonisation of the intestine with 'false' intestinal bacteria and these diseases can pass onto the next generation as a result of the intestinal miscolonisation. They claim that breastfeeding helps to provide beneficial bacteria that avoids these issues.

MOTHER'S MILK IS

- inexpensive.

- always has an optimal composition for your baby.

- is created and stored according to the 'demand regulates supply' principle.

- is easy to present to the baby and is 'always on the woman'.

- does not need any planning to have a sterile container and teat or sufficient milk powder.

- is always ready at the correct temperature.

Immediately after birth, the breast first produces protein-rich colostrum. Every drop of this precious treasure counts as it contains immunoglobulin A and other specific and non-specific antibodies. These are a huge help with immunising the baby against certain diseases. The small quantities of colostrum produced satisfy your baby's needs as her stomach is only about 2cm in diameter at birth.

The milk comes in between the 3rd and 5th day after the birth. The breast tissue is heavily supplied with blood during this time, which can result in heat and redness. The breasts can also become uncomfortable, hard and dry due to storage of tissue water caused by the increased secretion of lymph fluid.

THE HAPPY BREASTFEEDING CIRCLE

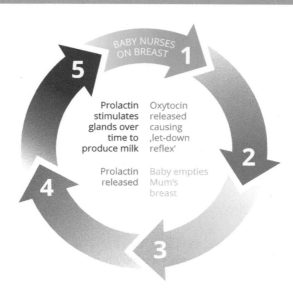

The breastfeeding demand and supply chain is circular. It starts with the baby suckling on Mum which stimulates the release of oxytocin which in turn releases the milk. The milk ducts widen and the muscles around them contract. This is known as the 'let-down reflex'.

The action of the milk leaving the breast stimulates the release of prolactin.

This works over time to stimulate the glands to generate milk that will be released when the baby nurses the breast again. This means that the baby's nursing in the afternoon sets the tone for the early morning feed.

The 'let-down reflex' is not necessarily noticeable, but can be perceived by Mum several times during breastfeeding as a tingling sensation or a slight stinging in the breast tissue.

Each time the baby feeds, the first milk he receives quenches his thirst. The longer the breast meal lasts, the richer / saturated with fat the milk becomes.

Prolactin

- causes milk formation.

- stimulates the growth of the mammary glands.

- induces milk depletion and maintains further milk production.

- also suppresses ovulation and menstruation, as long as your partner breastfeeds at regular intervals over 24 hours (day *and* night). However, this is *not* a reliable contraceptive guarantee!

Oxytocin

- also/better known as the 'cuddle hormone' as levels rise during cuddling.

- causes the milk to flow = 'let-down reflex'.

- stimulates the contraction of smooth muscles (uterus, milk ducts).

- stimulates secretion (nipples, vagina, uterus).

- is the perfect excuse to cuddle Mum!

Top tip: She's not going to be going anywhere once she's started a feeding session so set her up on the sofa and cuddle both of them!

The sooner your newborn baby is breastfed, the better the 'let-down reflex' will work. Putting the baby on the breast at least every three hours is the key to a successful breastfeeding relationship. You might have worked out that this means your partner will spend most of her time nursing and it can feel like a never-ending process, but it will pay off.

Breastfeeding is an economical system with minimal waste. The baby's demand regulates the supply of breast milk, regardless of whether the baby sucks or milk is pumped out with a breast pump. This means that the amount of milk in the early days of breastfeeding is increased by offering both breasts; later on, when the process works flawlessly, only one breast per breastfeeding meal keeps the amount of breast milk at level.

However, it appears that milk flow is subject to fluctuations at different times of the day and this can be influenced by stress. More stress means less milk is available.

A stress-reduced daily routine establishes a more successful breastfeeding relationship, especially in the six to eight weeks after birth. This is roughly the time it takes for a woman's reproductive system to return to its pre-pregnancy condition.

So, Mum is responsible for creating the baby, giving birth and breastfeeding. Your job is to do all you can to help set up a loving, stress-free environment for the first stage of your baby's life.

IS YOUR BABY A BARRACUDA OR A LITTLE LAMB?

Not every baby is alike. They already have their characteristics: one may drink fast and furiously like a little barracuda, another always takes his time meaning every feed is a long feed.

What sort of character does your baby have and how can you incorporate this into your daily structure? Many babies quickly pick up habits and routines and can easily get grumpy when we don't stick to the plan.

The happy nursing circle can be enhanced by creating your own circular rhythm with your baby:

nurse – nappy – entertain – sleep – repeat

Mum is almost exclusively engaged in these rhythms as the baby will nurse around 8–12 times every 24 hours in the first few days and weeks. This maintains the happy nursing circle and keeps the milk flowing.

Happy baby, happy parents.

LET'S GET TO THE POINT – NIPPLES

It's fair to say men generally like to know how things work. You saw your partner's nipples up close and personal before she became pregnant and you didn't notice any holes or delivery tubes. Yet when a cow is milked you see a steady stream of milk shooting out. So how do they work during breastfeeding?

There is no visible magic tube or hole. Did you know that each of the 15–25 breast lobes, also known as milk ducts, flows separately into the nipple? The milk leaks out of the cells of the nipple. This sometimes happens at impressive speed, especially when the baby hasn't fed for a while and the breast is full. While you have probably been admonished for being too rough with your partner's nipples during sex play you'll find that babies can be far rougher, especially when they start to develop teeth!

Paying close attention to your partner's nipples may not be as sexy as it used to be but it can save a lot of discomfort and may prevent breastfeeding finishing early.

During pregnancy your partner can help prepare her nipples with these simple actions:

- Washing her breasts daily with cool water, without soap.

- Drying her breasts carefully with a towel.

- Allowing escaping colostrum to dry to care for the nipple.

- Having the occasional bra-free day.

We're guessing you only paid attention to the last suggestion!

REPAIRING A BROKEN CYCLE

So what happens when things go wrong? It's not as if you can offer the baby your own nipple. You need to have a back-up plan if the milk bar is not available for whatever reason. Now that you know the happy breastfeeding cycle you can decide whether you both want to support Mum's natural 'software' with new hardware: breast pumps. Mum can use them if her breasts become overfull due to a light feed. You can then store the milk in the freezer. If you know that Mum is not going to be around for the next feed – she may just be shattered after a run of broken nights – you can defrost the milk and get it to room temperature ready for the feed.

Make sure you know how long milk can be stored in different conditions. According to the NHS you can keep breast milk in a fridge at 4°C for up to eight days. If you're not sure the fridge is as cold as 4°C only store it for up to three days. You can keep breast milk for up to two weeks in the ice compartment of a fridge or for up to six months in a freezer if it is -18°C or lower.

Once breast milk has been defrosted it needs to be used within two hours if kept at room temperature or within 24 hours in a fridge. Never refreeze breast milk.

Don't heat breast milk in the microwave or on the hob. Defrost it by putting the bag in lukewarm (body temperature) water.

You can also have formula milk available. The general rule is breast milk before formula, but if the breast milk is frozen and the baby is hungry NOW it's better for everyone if you make up some formula.

Stating the obvious (again) but it would really help if you practiced all the steps involved in making up formula milk before you need to do it in battle conditions. A desperately screaming baby is not conducive to following step-by-step instructions for the first time!

Jobs for
SUPERHERO DADS

You may have been best friends and lovers before the arrival of your bundle of joy but now you have new responsibilities. Or rather, one very small responsibility that creates a maelstrom of mini liabilities! You are now partners in crime. It's time to play Batwoman and Robin. You have to play the supporting role because your Batwoman doesn't even need a utility belt. She has sneakily kept her magic feeding devices under her cape all this time.

So it's time to slip your underpants on over your trousers (if only to make your Batwoman laugh after a long, exhausting night) and take on some new challenging roles:

CHAUFFEUR

Who needs a Batmobile when you've got a ... sling! Pop your baby superhero in a sling for lots of bonding skin contact as you explore Gotham City together (are we taking this analogy too far yet?) The more time you spend with your child between breastfeeding phases, the stronger your dad–baby relationship will become. The other advantage of the sling is that you shield the baby from any over-eager attention from curious passers-by.

Some dads feel self-conscious carrying a baby in a sling, as if it is somehow not a 'manly' activity. This is obviously nonsense, but stereotypes still exist for some people. What you might not expect is that lots of women you pass will smile and strike up conversations with you. They certainly don't think you are not being manly.

If you really want to attract condescending looks from both men and women, try walking through a town centre carrying an ironing board. It's strange, but true!

MASTER OF DISTRACTION

There are two types of people in the world. Those who have lots of really important advice to tell you about raising a baby and those who are not at all interested in babies. You will get the benefit of hearing an awful lot of advice, or maybe a lot of awful advice. You will definitely receive conflicting advice. Of course, you will listen to other people's opinions but you don't have to put up with them being turned into direct orders.

If your partner is being blasted with advice you know she doesn't want to hear, it's time to use your superhero charm to deflect it or change the subject. You can also revert to your bouncer role and find a reason to escort them from the premises. If both of these tactics fail to work you are experiencing a hardcore bad advice giver. They are probably also a family member or a close friend. In this case it can be useful to take one for the team and act the idiot (or the Joker?) so you make Mum laugh and diffuse the situation.

Another way of taking one for the team is to behave as if the issue being discussed is one you personally have very strong feelings about and that you have researched it. If there's a debate to be had it does not have to include Mum.

You can also smooth off a lot of rough edges by admitting that you might be a bit overprotective but this is very important to you. It's harder to argue with that as you are offering them the 'higher ground'. If they remind you of it a few years down the line you can share a conspiratorial smile with your partner.

Another tactic is blatant distraction. If the advice givers are from previous generations ask them about the theories that were around when they were new parents. The changes in advice – and often the return of old, previously scorned advice – can be fascinating. It can be concluded with something along the lines of "Oh well, we tend to do it this way now".

Whatever the outcome you have the right to raise your baby the way you want to and Mum doesn't need to be involved in any heated discussions on the subject.

As an example, let's assume you and your partner have decided the baby will sleep in the same room as you. You've researched this extensively and are happy with your decision. However, your mother-in-law is aghast that her new grandson is not going to be sleeping in a separate room.

We're choosing the mother-in-law example purely because this is the person who, due to family dynamics, is probably the least likely to want to discuss this situation with you, rather than her daughter. To be clear, this mother-in-law is only arguing her case because she genuinely believes that keeping the baby in his own room will bring much-needed benefits to the new family of three.

Here are some possible conversations:

MIL: Both of our children slept in their own room when they were babies and they all developed healthy sleep patterns. My brother kept his twins in his bedroom and they didn't sleep through until they were two! He was a wreck from lack of sleep! The same happened with my friend Miranda.

You: We've chosen to do this because the midwife told us that this way tends to be the most successful way out all of the new mums she has seen.

Or:

You: We've researched it a lot and we have decided this is the best approach for us as a family.

Or:

You: This is the way it tends to be done now. These things seem to go in phases, don't they? Is it true that your parents' generation used to dip a dummy in brandy to encourage them to go to sleep?

Or:

You: Honestly? We think it's the best way, but the reality is that I can't sleep if the baby is not in the room. I keep worrying that I can't hear if he's okay. It's silly but that's how it is. I can't function without sleep.

Or:

Okay then. Let's have a bet. If the baby quickly develops a steady sleeping pattern, you have to tell everyone that I'm the best dad in the world. If she doesn't, I have to tell everyone you're the best mother-in-law in the world.

Or you can take your mother-in-law aside and explain that you've both decided on this course of action and you really need her to run with it to keep everything calm for mum.

CHILD ENTERTAINER

If this is not your first child and you've already got a little monster zooming around the place, you can bet they will demand attention the moment the newcomer latches onto the nipple. Be on hand, or make plans for entertaining or distracting the first born. Children's TV can be a life-saver as long as it doesn't drive your partner to distraction while she is feeding! Around five or six in the afternoon is often a difficult phase. The first child can be cranky, the baby is overwhelmed from new impressions and needs comfort besides being hungry. Mum is often exhausted so calmness and milk can be scarce resources as mum's stress level is high.

You know those couples where the baby is handed to the mum whenever it is upset because the dad has no idea how to solve the problem? Don't be one of those dads! Spend time with the baby in your new family unit. Discover the reasons for its strange little moods together (or at least try to!) It can be very draining for Mum being the sole person who can calm the baby. You sometimes see families in a restaurant with a grumpy baby where the mum spends the whole time jiggling the baby while the rest of the family eats. The mum should be the priority – she should eat first.

LIBRARIAN

Maybe your idea of a librarian is a stuffy man in an ancient tweed jacket with elbow pads. Or has your memory taken you to memories of Rachel Weisz in the film The Mummy? Stop that right now! It's time to get focused. The modern librarian uses the internet to look up information and get  advice from experts. The NHS has lots of useful information. A simple online search on key terms like 'breastfeeding advice' should bring up lots of useful sources.

It can also be helpful to hear from other new parents who are experiencing similar problems in online chat groups. Just be warned that many of the subjects discussed in these areas can be both shocking and hilarious!

APPOINTMENT COORDINATOR

The baby has arrived and everyone wants to see the new little bundle of joy, to remark on how tiny its little fingers are and discuss the colour of newborn baby poo in tiresome detail. This can be the last thing you need when you are getting to grips with this massive upheaval in your lives with minimal sleep.

The ideal scenario is to only invite people who are fantastic cooks and who will bring you delicious goodies to sustain you through this exciting time. If your immediate family and closest friends fit this brief then congratulations! You're going to enjoy this phase more than the average new parents.

Otherwise you're just going to have to do what everyone else does and manage the flow of visitors. It's not unreasonable to ask everyone other than immediate family to wait a while before meeting your new superstar. It is also not unreasonable to prevent immediate family members from staying over at your house just after the baby is born. That doesn't mean it won't be controversial! If there is an issue with someone (who often genuinely believes they are helping) just as Mum is trying to get the hang of breastfeeding it needs to be resolved by you.

Visitors need to fit in around the new baby routines, not the other way around. If it's not convenient for someone to pop round at a certain time, ask them to come when it is easier for your family.

You may also have to act as time-enforcer as people nearly always lose track of time when they are cooing over a baby. You don't want people staying too long, interrupting times when Mum could be having a nap or a shower before the next feed.

NURSE

Doctors may get all the credit in a hospital, but nurses are superheroes without capes too. You are the person who really knows your partner so you're the best judge of whether she may be starting to get depressed, or if she is just exhausted. You can also be the slightly annoying person who nags her to drink or eat enough or make sure she is taking sufficient pain relief at the right time, provide time away from the baby (and visitors) to have a shower, or just to do something for herself for a change. Bed baths, role play and any dressing up is strictly optional at this stage!

BATH ATTENDANT

Because who wouldn't want to hand a newly fed baby to a loving partner and step into a relaxing bath? If the baby has a nap you can grab a moment to wash your partner's back! Mum might also need a hand getting in and out of the bath if she has stitches after the birth.

But it's not just Mum who needs a bath. You can spend fun time with the little one by bathing him. You can also build up more skin-to-skin time by being in the bath with the baby.

This requires maternal trust in the father's abilities – and it is a good way of letting you as Dad have experience of complete responsibility for the baby.

When you get visitors to see the new baby you will probably notice how fresh they look. They may have the audacity to arrive without bags under their eyes. They might even be dressed in something other than pyjamas or jogging bottoms. What they will

have is their phone to take photos to put on social media! If this is going to upset your partner try to make time for her to tidy herself up before the visit. Or make an effort to stage manage the photographs. You can also ask them to just post pictures of themselves and the new baby.

Alternatively, you can point out to your partner that the only new parents who look good are the couples in the celebrity magazines and they have makeup artists and Photoshop specialists. There should be no pressure for any new parents to 'look good' for social media. We have only pointed this out in case this sort of thing will really matter to your partner.

CHEF DE CUISINE

We joked about only inviting fantastic cooks around but there is merit in the idea of getting people to bring certain food with them. It's frustrating if you have filled the freezer with easy-to-cook food only to see it being consumed by your guests. Indulge your superhero sneaky powers here by using comments such as "We absolutely loved your shepherd's pie!" to get them to bring what you really want so you don't get the same from everyone. It will also give the cook a feeling of satisfaction knowing she has nourished Mum, and thus the baby at such an important time. If they take the dirty baking tray away with them afterwards, so much the better!

As time goes by you will make friends with other new parents. It can help to have meals together sometimes so you can share your food as well as the experiences of looking after a baby. You should be doing as much of the food buying, preparation and cooking as possible during the baby honeymoon. These meals

should be nourishing and easy to cook. If your cooking repertoire is limited get hold of some easy-to-follow cook books and concentrate on serving up comfort food. You can spice things up a bit later when you have more time.

There are lots of food ideas in our Soul food for new families chapter.

MASSEUR

If you're going to be a truly 'hands-on' dad you've got to be, well, hands-on. We've described some key massage techniques in the next section, so make sure your hands are warm!

Gentle
BREASTFEEDING
MASSAGE

If you've been paying attention so far, you will be up to speed with the key messages of this book:

1. Stress is bad as it can reduce milk production.

2. Cuddles are good as they can boost milk production.

It doesn't take a genius to work out that a tender, soothing massage is going to help the breastfeeding cause. The breastfeeding massage we outline below lowers cortisol levels which lowers stress hormones and stimulates happiness hormones, as well as supporting the self-healing powers of the body.

It also stimulates blood circulation, lymph flow and slight detoxification (this causes no harm and doesn't affect the breast milk), metabolism and circulation. It releases tension and blockages and improves muscle flexibility. This all results in the breast milk flowing more easily.

However, before you get too excited, we need to point out that you will be massaging your partner's back, not her breasts!

A breastfeeding massage is easy to perform and will take about 15 minutes. You just need a little time in advance to familiarise yourself with the simple steps.

You can either gently massage over a T-shirt or perform it on naked skin. With the latter option you can use olive oil. Use better quality olive oil if you can afford it, organic and extra virgin is best, as the body absorbs some of the contents of the oil through the skin. The oil nourishes your partner's skin and helps you to give a really gentle massage.

You don't need any special props apart from two chairs with a flat surface. One for you and for your partner. However, she can rest her forearms on a cushion or a nursing pillow for extra comfort.

This sequence of massage steps is coordinated in the perfect way to stimulate the lymphatic system while relaxing and relieving muscle tension.

We're not going to dazzle you with science here, but it's important to perform the steps in this order without omitting any of them to get the maximum benefit.

The first step – opening the lymph filter – 'opens the door' and encourages the drainage of the lymphatic system. The remaining steps persuade everything to move in the right direction.

- Remember the happy baby, happy parents mantra? Timing is key! Choose a slot where the baby is well-fed, changed and happy – so both of you can settle into this partner time activity.

- Make sure the room is pleasantly warm.

- Create an inviting room atmosphere. This doesn't need to involve fancy extras like candles.

- Ensure privacy (switch off your phone – and yes, this includes all socials and texts).

- Take off jewellery.

- Both of you should drink a glass of water or tea so you're hydrated for the massage session.

- Your partner should go to the bathroom before the massage.

- If you massage with oil – place it within easy reach, using a pump bottle or a dispenser to avoid mess.

- Always ensure both you and your partner are comfortably positioned before starting the massage.

- Follow the steps according to the treatment scheme.

- Remember that rhythmic movements work best in a massage.

- You did remember to warm your hands, didn't you?

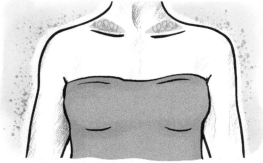

POSITIONING

Your partner sits comfortably on a stool.

You stand behind her.

MASSAGE AREA

The massage focuses on the triangle shaped structure (the terminus), just above the collar bones, marked on the diagram.

HAND POSITION

With your palms pointing downwards, work the area with the first section of your index and middle fingers.

MASSAGE MOVEMENT

Touch the area very gently with your fingers as shown by the arrows in the second diagram. Use your fingers as if you are swimming breaststroke, moving from the inside to the outside of the little triangle, and caressing rather than applying pressure. Imagine you are gently melting a crumb of chocolate with your finger.

PRESSURE

very gentle

TIME FRAME

1–2 minutes

2

If your partner has low blood pressure you need to be very careful when applying this massage step. You will need to limit the moves to a maximum of 3–5 sets to each side of the neck to avoid her feeling faint. If her blood pressure is normal, you can do 5–7 sets on each side.

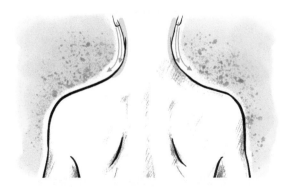

POSITIONING

You're standing side on at shoulder level with your partner. Make sure your body centre and her body side form a line, i.e. your belly button and her shoulders are on one line.

By extending your front arm horizontally, she can comfortably lean her forehead against the inside of your forearm. This means she can relax her neck muscles while you perform the massage step from both sides.

MASSAGE AREA

You are working on the outside of the neck.

HAND POSITION

The palm of your working hand faces downwards. Spread your thumb so it is 90 degrees to your fingers. Perform 5 quick downward strokes (= 1 set) with the outer edge of your index finger. You should hear a soft "scraping" sound.

MASSAGE MOVEMENT AND DIRECTION

Each stroke starts at the mastoid, (the little knob behind the ear). When you start the movement, the tip of your index finger touches the ear. Stroke vertically downwards until you touch her shoulder. Make sure that the 4 short movements (the shorter, inside arrow) go to the shoulder. The fifth stroke (outside arrow) goes from the starting point to the little triangle you worked on in Step 1.

Work the other side accordingly.

PRESSURE

very gentle

FREQUENCY

3-7 sets on each side (depending on blood pressure)

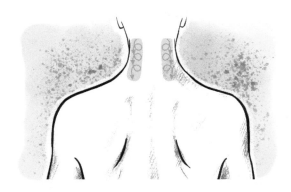

POSITIONING

Keep your basic position from Step 2, but you might want to move slightly to ensure you are comfortable.

Your forearm remains where it is and gently supports your partner's forehead.

MASSAGE AREA

Either side of the back of the neck.

HAND POSITION

Bring the tips of your thumb and index finger to the same height to form a U-shape. The fingertips guide the movement.

MASSAGE MOVEMENT

Place your thumb and index finger at the base of the skull and follow the movement shown in the diagram, forming circles that lead downwards to the base of the neck. Repeat these gentle circles from the starting point until the neck feels more relaxed.

PRESSURE

gentle

FREQUENCY

5 to 10 times

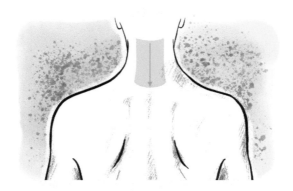

4

POSITIONING

Keep your sidewards position. It's easiest for you and most relaxing for your partner if your belly button and her shoulders are in one line.

Hold your front arm out in a 90-degree angle, so she can lean her forehead against it.

MASSAGE AREA

The central line of the back of the neck.

HAND POSITION

With the palm of your hand facing downwards, spread your thumb so that the webbing between thumb and index finger is stretched. You use this webbing membrane to sweep the spine gently as you move down the neck.

MASSAGE MOVEMENT

Touch the top vertebra and gently move your hand downwards allowing the webbing membrane to stroke the spine. Stop at the base of the neck.

PRESSURE

gentle

FREQUENCY

5-10 times

5

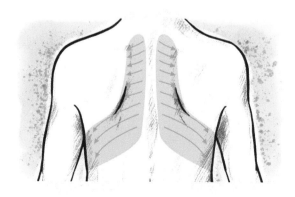

POSITIONING

Stand sideways to your partner with your massaging hand on her upper back. Rest the other hand on her upper arm.

MASSAGE AREA

Between the shoulder blades and the back of the ribs.

HAND POSITION

Start with your first two fingers spread a rib-width apart and use them to 'comb' the ribs, as shown on the diagram. For the stroke below the shoulder blade, hold your hand in a cupping position by placing all the fingers and the thumb together, thus creating a hollow hand. Your left hand works on the left side of the body. When you switch sides, stand and work the right side with your right hand.

MASSAGE MOVEMENT

Make 2 strokes by positioning the fingertips beyond the spine and gently push the fingers outwards along the spaces between the ribs, until the fingertips touch the shoulder blade. The last stroke is made below the shoulder blade.

PRESSURE

hard enough so you can feel tissue movement

FREQUENCY

5-10 times each side

POSITIONING

Sit within half an arm's length behind your partner and make sure you are comfortable.

You work with both hands at the same time.

MASSAGE AREA

From the bra line upwards to the shoulder, on either side of the back of the spine.

HAND POSITION

Your fingers point upwards, the thumbs are slightly apart. Only the outside of your thumbs touch the back.

MASSAGE MOVEMENT

Work up from your partner's bra line to the top of her shoulders, make circles with the outer halves of your thumbs between the spine and shoulder blades.

PRESSURE

gentle

TIME FRAME

1-2 minutes

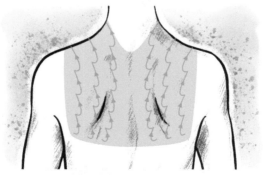

POSITIONING

Remain sitting within half an arm's length behind your partner.

As in Step 5, put all fingers together to perform a cupping movement.

MASSAGE AREA

The upper back.

HAND POSITION

Cup your hands with your fingers pointing upwards. Your thumb, the heel of your hand and little finger are always in contact with your partner's back.

The other fingers should stretch upwards in a cater-pillar-like movement.

MASSAGE MOVEMENT

Place the palm of your hands just below your partner's shoulder blades. Perform the caterpillar-like movements along the entire width of the upper back up to her shoulders.

PRESSURE

gentle

TIME FRAME

1-2 minutes

POSITIONING

Remain seated behind your partner.

MASSAGE AREA

The entire upper back.

HAND POSITION

The Leap frog combines three hand positions: First spread your fingers so your palms lie flat on your partner's upper back until they seem to suck to her skin. Now release the tension from your fingers and feel the vacuum created by the palms of your hands. Release this vacuum by lifting the centre of the hand before releasing your hand completely from the back.

MASSAGE MOVEMENT

Start at your partner's bra line and perform the move upwards over her entire upper back. Be careful not to push your partner forward when placing your hands.

There will only be a very subtle suction effect if you're working without oil. When you use oil you can hear a 'smacking' sound when you lift your hand from her skin.

PRESSURE

gentle

TIME FRAME

1-2 minutes

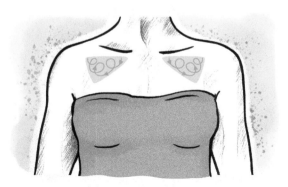

9

POSITIONING

Stand behind your partner just as you did in Step 1.

MASSAGE AREA

With this step you focus on the small triangle below the collar bone as shown on the diagram.

HAND POSITION

Your palms point downwards. Work the area with the first section of your index and middle fingers.

MASSAGE MOVEMENT

Perform the move very gently as if you were swimming breaststroke (the left hand works in counter-clockwise circles, the right hand clockwise).

PRESSURE

very gentle

TIME FRAME

1-2 minutes

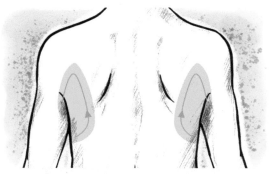

POSITIONING

Place both hands a little higher than your partner's waist, starting off with the palms of your hands facing each other.

MASSAGE AREA

From the lower rib above the waist to the armpits.

HAND POSITION

Your thumbs point upwards, the palms touch the ribcage.

MASSAGE MOVEMENT

Place both hands slightly above the waist so the palms face each other. Your hands gently lift the tissue in an upward motion towards the armpits. The stroke ends when your index fingers touch the inside of the upper arm.

PRESSURE

firm enough not to tickle your partner!

FREQUENCY

up to 10 times

These ten steps are quite a lot to remember, especially when you've got your partner in your hands rather than this book. Hopefully this summary will be useful while you're getting the hang of the techniques:

1

Clearing the inner lymph filter areas

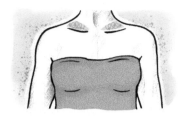

1–2 minutes

2

Clearing cervical lymph

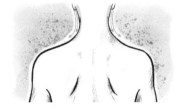

3–5 sets each side

Be careful if your partner has low blood pressure.

3

Spin round the neck

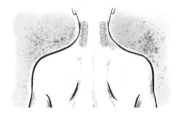

5–10 times

4

Gentle drainage of the neck

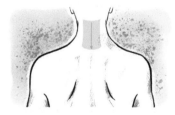

5–10 times

5

Loosen back tension

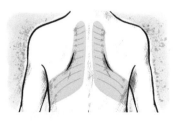

Up to 10 times each side

6

Circle the upper back extensor muscles

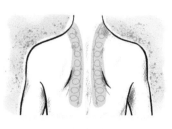

8–10 times

7

Cupped caterpillar

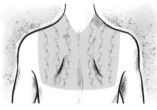

1–2 minutes

8

Leap frog

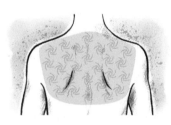

1–2 minutes

9

Clearing the outer lymph filter areas

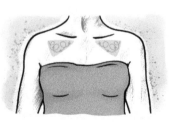

1–2 minutes

10

Release tension in the shoulder girdle

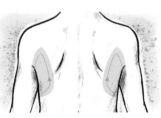

Up to 10 times

SOUL FOOD
for new families

There was probably a point early in your relationship with your partner where you took her out for a fancy meal and tried not to stare at her breasts too much. Now we want you to focus on delivering regular delicious and nutritious meals that fuel your partner's breast milk. Ironic, eh?

Fortunately women don't need to eat lots of strange delicacies in order to produce the right amount of milk. They just need to eat a healthy, balanced diet and we've summarised this below:

- At least five portions of fruit or vegetables a day – not the same few every day – and only one glass of 100% juice per day (this basically means no cheating).

- Protein, which can come from various sources – chicken and lean meat, fish, eggs, pulses, soya, seeds, and nuts.

- Carbohydrates – bread, pasta and rice (brown if possible), and potatoes.

- Calcium sources – milk, cheese, yoghurt, or vegan options such as brown bread, pulses, tofu, and dried fruit.

- Fibre – it's a good idea for new mums to have lots of fibre as they can be prone to bowel problems and constipation (romantic, eh?). This is mainly covered by the foods mentioned above, but wholemeal bread and pasta, rice, pulses, breakfast cereal, fruit and vegetables are good sources.

There are bookcases full of dietary advice for pregnant and breastfeeding women so we are going to focus our advice on spending time getting organised so everything can run as smoothly as possible. You can also return to the 'village raising a baby' concept and request home-cooked food you both like when people ask what they can buy the new baby. It would be much more helpful than yet another baby-grow they will grow out of in a few weeks.

The ideal time to start is while your partner is going through the so-called 'nest-building' phase in the third trimester of her pregnancy. Your life will become full of fancy baby gadgets, but it's also a good time to start stocking the freezer with pre-cooked delights in suitable portions. You won't want to be dashing to the supermarket just after the baby arrives. Filling your cupboards takes priority over practising taking sharp corners inside the house with an empty new pram!

Just a quick word on 'dietary advice' before we move on. Some new mums may be in a hurry to try and lose 'extra weight' they might have gained during pregnancy. Going on a restricted diet when breastfeeding is counterproductive. It is much better to have well-balanced nutrition to provide for mum and baby.

Mum can eat what she likes, within reason, and can go back to enjoying those foods (like blue cheese) that she had to avoid during pregnancy. However, you might find that your baby seems to have a sensitivity to certain foods. This is often in the form of diarrhoea but could also be demonstrated by them being more irritable than usual. If this happens you can save some spectacularly messy nappies by checking if there are patterns of a particular food causing an explosive rear end reaction!

CUPBOARD love

So what are the best things to have in your cupboards that are healthy and also support milk production? It's not too different to what many people who follow a healthy diet have, but here are some suggestions:

- Unsweetened cereals

- Wholewheat pasta

- Wholegrain bread

- Salty crackers

- Skimmed milk

- Fat-free cottage cheese

- Low-fat, naturally sweetened yoghurt – or dairy-free alternatives such as almond, cashew or coconut yoghurt

- Parmesan cheese

- Fresh farm eggs for protein-rich omelettes, or hard-boiled and ready-to-eat

- Natural peanut butter

- Pure fruit jams

- Raisins, dates and other dried fruits

- Seeds

- Almonds

- (Wholemeal) rice – a good source of energy, which is both hearty and sweet

- Couscous and millet, as both can quickly be prepared

- High quality oils such as olive oil (extra virgin) and coconut oil

- The plant milk of your choice

- Potatoes – they can be prepared for several meals and can also be used cold in a salad or the next day as chips.

FRESH is king

Fresh fruit and vegetables are always good for us. Go seasonal, local and organic wherever possible. You might want to test individually what Mum (and indirectly the baby) can tolerate. Make sure you include vegetables you can eat raw such as carrots, cucumbers, celery and tomatoes.

You might be complaining about double standards here. We told you to get extra supplies in but fresh food can't be stored for long. One solution is to sign up for a veggie box scheme so you have fresh veg delivered to your door. Alternatively, many products such as berries and spinach can be bought frozen and used when they are needed.

Little **SNACKS**

- Breastfeeding cookies – you can buy these in specialist shops or make them yourself. They provide high levels of calcium.

- Dates

- Dried fruits

- Fruit bars

- Muesli bars

- 'Power balls' – no giggling please!
  We've got the recipe for these later in the book.

These nibbles are also perfect to pack for the birth itself as they are suitable for everyone, including you and the midwife. Just do us a favour and don't sneak off to check out your chest if you've been eating breastfeeding cookies. Or the contents of your pants if you've been eating power balls!

MILK BOOSTERS

You might be surprised by how many ingredients may stimulate milk production. There is something for every mum on this list.

- Almond milk

- Almond and nut kernels (these become easier to digest if you put them in water overnight to initiate the germination process)

- Aniseed

- Benedictine herb

- Borage leaves

- Caraway seeds

- Chicory coffee

- Coconut

- Coriander

- Dill

- Fennel seed

- Fenugreek seeds

- Ghee

- Milk thistle

- Raisins

- Sesame seeds

- Sloe juice

- Sunflower seeds

Heart-warming
TOPPINGS

Many beneficial ingredients can be used as healthy toppings to add interest to other food. The secret of the delicious crunch of pumpkin seeds, sunflower seeds, flaked almonds and nut kernels is the dry roasting. The good news is that you can prepare them in advance and store them in jam jars.

Pumpkin seeds and sunflower seeds enhance any green salad and taste great over potato soup or added to rice. Roasted hazelnuts are a super snack and almond flakes give any muesli or sweet dish a particularly luxurious touch, but also taste wonderful over steamed cauliflower.

To roast the toppings, heat a pan on low heat and add your nut or seed mixture, stirring occasionally until it is roasted. There is no need to add oil.
Be sure to let them cool down before enjoying them.

GOWRI'S TURMERIC TOP-UP

Mix ¼ teaspoon of turmeric powder with a little honey and eat this twice a day.

It's not only delicious but it is also helpful when muscles, ligaments and joints feel tender and fluid-logged. Birth and postpartum Guru Dr Gowri Motha claims it is also a good remedy for acute and chronic coughs.

TIPPLES
for nipples

Your partner will need plenty of fluids after giving birth and it's important that a breastfeeding mother keeps her body hydrated by drinking whenever she is thirsty. Still water (with and without fruit), thin juice spritzer or just hot water, or in times of more breast milk demand, even 'breastfeeding tea' are all excellent for hydrating Mum.

Breastfeeding tea is not a fancy blend you can expect to pick up in your local coffee shop – although it might be possible one day. It should only be served at times when your baby needs more breast

milk to be satisfied, for example due to a growth spurt.

You can buy breastfeeding tea in specialist shops online or you can prepare it yourself. Mum should not drink more than three large cups spread over the day.

Ingredients:

- 1 part caraway, aniseed and fennel seeds
- 1 part fenugreek
- 1 part lemon verbena leaves
- 1 part elderflowers (can be used as fresh blossoms or in dried form from health food shops)

Preparation:

Brew two teaspoons of the mixture with 250ml of boiling water, cover and let it sit for 10 minutes. Strain and sweeten if necessary.

All-day
BREAKFAST
IDEAS and snacks

Hmmm, an all-day breakfast conjures images of a late start to the day, probably after having a bit too much booze. When breastfeeding it's possible to have a number of breakfasts, especially when the day might start very early after a broken night's sleep. Here we present a range of healthy breakfasts and snacks that will keep Mum (and you) in good shape for feeding your little one.

Pick and choose what appeals to you and if cooking them feels too much like hard work you can always ask the grandparents to provide some for you. Especially the 'powerballs', as they are pretty much the perfect food for breastfeeding mums.

GOOD OLD PORRIDGE

Get creative and figure out what toppings you like best!

Try different toppings on different days to get a variety of nutrients and flavours:

- Cinnamon
- Frozen berries
- Honey
- Raisins
- Shredded coconut
- Sliced apple
- Toasted almonds
- Walnuts

Rich and more decadent than the regular version, semolina porridge is creamy and delicious and will please anyone's sweet tooth.

Ingredients for 4 portions:

- 6 tbps semolina (you can also use spelt semolina)
- 1000 ml milk (of your choice)
- 1 tbsp maple syrup or brown sugar
- 1 tbsp coconut oil
- Pinch of salt
- Pinch of vanilla

Preparation:

1. Combine the milk, salt and maple syrup and heat it (do not boil).

2. Once the mixture is hot, add the semolina while stirring.

3. Turn the heat down and continue to stir.

4. The semolina porridge will thicken quickly. Remove it from the heat when it reaches your preferred texture.

Semolina porridge can be eaten warm or cold.

Alternatively, why not try a nice rice pudding with cinnamon and brown sugar?

These are a great cold alternative to porridge.

Ingredients per portion:

- 30 grams oats
- 180 ml milk or plant milk of your choice
- 1 tbsp chia seeds

Preparation:

Simply mix before going to bed and top with the fruit of your choice the next morning.

CHIA PUDDING

For one serving combine 1 tbsp of chia seeds with 6 tablespoons of a liquid of your choice.

Talking of dad jokes … Powerballs are also called breastfeeding balls, milk balls or milk-stimulating, or postpartum nutrition balls.

These powerballs are the ideal gift for the first visit to celebrate the new family. They can be stored well in the refrigerator in a box – and can even be frozen and taken out for daily servings.

They are not just liked by new mums, but by their partners so don't hold back in trying them! The original recipe comes from Ingeborg Stadelmann's book 'A consultation with a midwife' and these powerballs have migrated into many mouths.

Ingredients:

- 500 grams spelt grain (you can get this at health food shops)
- 200 grams cooked wholegrain rice
- 150 grams ghee
- 150 grams honey
- 100 grams almonds (unpeeled)
- Water

Preparation:

1. Coarsely grind the spelt and dry roast it (without oil) in a large pan until it is slightly brown.

2. Then roast the unpeeled almonds in the pan and grind finely. (Alternatively you can use ground almonds and omit the roasting step.)

3. Mix the ghee and honey.

4. Mix the still warm grain with the remaining ingredients.

5. Carefully add water (approximately 3/4 glass), mix well, and put the mixture in the fridge overnight.

The next day form small balls of about 1.5–2cm in diameter. This works best with wetted hands. The balls have a rather crumbly consistency due to the spelt. Once the balls are finished you can cover them – for the benefit of the eye and tongue. You can use brown sugar, dark cocoa powder or coconut flakes. If you're really posh, coat them in a layer of chocolate.

The balls are suitable for freezing. Simply take the next day's serving (3–4 pieces) out of the freezer the evening before to defrost.

We like the original version. The ghee in combination with the roasted components gives the powerballs a caramel note; the wild honey adds a discreetly sweet taste. In theory there are no limits to your imagination when it comes to powerball ingredients. However, avoid sage and, some say, peppermint as they slow down production of breast milk.

Ingredients:

- 250 grams rolled oats
- 100 grams slivered almonds
- 1/2 tsp salt
- 60 grams coconut oil
- 75 grams cranberries
- 50 grams pumpkin seeds
- 100 grams honey (liquid)
- real vanilla

Preparation:

1. Preheat the oven to 180°C.

2. Melt the coconut oil on low heat in a pan.

3. Line a baking tray with baking paper.

4. Mix all the ingredients in a bowl and spread on the tray. Bake for 8 minutes at first.

5. Then turn the mixture and bake for another 5 minutes until crispy.

6. Turn it over again if necessary (it depends how thick the mixture is) and bake for another 2–3 minutes.

7. Let the granola cool down.
   Store in a swing top jar for easy access.

This crunchy muesli serves as a muesli variation, as topping for yoghurt, or as a crispy layer in a fancy trifle (yoghurt or mascarpone, granola and apple sauce).

A DATE WITH DATES

You can get a headstart with your dad jokes here by asking Mum if she would like a date. This recipe makes 4 generous portions.

Ingredients:

- 250 grams Medjool dates, soaked overnight
- Juice and rind of 1 lemon (organic)
- 1 tbsp maple syrup
- 250 ml natural yoghurt
  (try to use Greek-style sheep's yoghurt instead of cow's or your choice of dairy alternative)
- Cinnamon

Preparation:

1. Simmer the dates in a little water to soften.

2. Drain off any excess fluid and then liquidise the dates until you have a thick puree.

3. Add all other ingredients and blend again.

4. Pour the mixture into serving dishes and refrigerate until you are ready to serve.

Who doesn't love scones with cream and jam? The good news is that their delicious mix of protein and carbohydrates (which include a hit of sugar) is fantastic for breastfeeding refuelling. They're pretty good for hands-on dads too. Just don't get involved with the age-old debate of whether to put the jam or cream on first!

This recipe comes from Russ's wife, Liz, who now regularly makes them at short notice to placate ravenous teenagers!

Ingredients:

- 600 grams self-raising flour
- 2 tbsps icing sugar
- 60 grams butter
- 375 ml milk

Preparation:

1. Preheat the oven to 220°C and grease a large baking tray.

2. Sift the flour and sugar into a large bowl.

3. Rub in the butter with your fingertips to get a consistent mix.

4. Make a well in the middle of the mixture and pour in the milk.

5. Mix the milk into the mixture by cutting it with a knife until you get a soft, sticky, smooth dough. The aim is to work the mixture as little as possible. If it's too sticky add a touch of water.

6. Press the dough out to 2cm thickness and, using a 4–5cm round cutter, cut as many rounds as you can out of the mixture.

7. Gently knead the remaining dough and repeat the above step until you have cut as many rounds as possible.

8. Place the scones on the baking tray and brush their surfaces with milk.

9. Bake the scones for 15 minutes or until the tops have browned and they sound hollow when they are tapped on the top.

10. Leave to cool (or for as long as you can wait) and spread with clotted cream and jam.

Leftover scones can be stored in an airtight container.

CRISPBREAD WITH A DIFFERENCE

Ingredients:

- 150 grams flour (or gluten-free bread mix)
- 150 grams ground almonds
- 100 grams pumpkin seeds (or mixed seeds from pumpkin seeds, sesame etc.)
- 150 grams sunflower seeds
- 100 grams crushed linseed (or 2 tablespoons psyllium as an alternative)
- 1 tsp salt

Preparation:

1. Mix the dry ingredients and stir with approximately 500 ml water to a 'dough' and allow to soak (you may want to add a little more water).

2. Preheat the oven to 180°C.

3. Line a large baking tray with baking paper and spread the mixture thinly.

4. Bake for 20 minutes.

5. Remove from the oven briefly and cut into pieces (use either a knife or a pizza cutter).

6. Then return to the oven and bake for another 5–10 minutes.

7. Remove from the tray, let it cool down and store in a tin.

BEETROOT DIP

Ingredients:

- 500 grams cooked beetroot
- 50 grams tender oat flakes
- 1 tbsp honey
- 50 ml olive oil
- 2 tbsp tahini (sesame paste)
- 5 tbsp lemon juice
- Salt and pepper

Preparation:

1. Puree everything, fill into jars and store in the refrigerator.

2. Can be served with tortilla chips or crispy bread.

SOUP for the postpartum soul

The emotional mix of joy, sorrow, excitement and unaccustomed sleep deprivation for both parents can wear on the nerves. A comforting home-made soup – often made from whatever is left in the fridge – is an ideal way to soothe them. There's one condition here: no straining off the vegetables to get a clear broth. Leave the ingredients in so the soup is rich in collagen. By adding starchy vegetables such as (sweet) potatoes or squash, you get a rich consistency when you purée the soup. You might want to triple your recipes and freeze the leftovers.

The soup itself can also be frozen. Leftover plastic take-away tubs make ideal containers as they provide a useful portion size. Should you use jars, leave 4cm to the edge of the jar space and put the lid on loosely until the soup has expanded and frozen. Then you can tighten the lid. The soup will keep for three months, but you're bound to feel the urge for it before then. To unfreeze, simply place the jar in the refrigerator overnight and the next day you can serve a soup that is not only delicious, but also invigorating.

There are a million recipes for soup, ranging from those featuring a key ingredient to 'empty the fridge soup'. The basic essential is to first cook your base ingredients (such as onions, carrots, celery, leeks, celeriac etc), along with some herbs in a little oil for 5 to 10 minutes to build up some flavour. Then add the other ingredients and water or stock and boil it up.
If you put the carcass from a roast chicken in the freezer when you have finished with it, you can defrost it anytime you get the urge to make soup.

The END – and the BEGINNING

So you've reached the end of this book. You might be still awaiting the arrival of your baby or maybe the stork has already left you a bundle of joy. Your partner and baby may take to breastfeeding effortlessly or it might simply just not work out. Breastfeeding does have many health benefits for both Mum and baby, but it's not the end of the world if it doesn't happen in the way you both wanted.

Being a parent is all about seeing the whole picture and breastfeeding is just a pixel in that picture. Many mums report feeling as if they have failed if they cannot breastfeed their child but this is simply not the case. How can you have failed if you've produced a wonderful new life?

We hope this book has been useful as you start out in your new family adventure. You have lots of funny moments to look forward to, sometimes sheer lack of sleep can bring humour to the strangest of things!

One thing we need to make very clear is that by writing this book for new dads, we mean no disrespect or criticism to all the wonderful new mums. We just wanted to create a short, accessible book for those fathers who may not find it so easy to establish a positive role in the new family.

Wishing you warm glows, guests bringing home-cooked lasagne, regular sleep patterns and lots of dad jokes. Remember that dad jokes are the ultimate dad accessory as no-one expects them to be funny! But it's inappropriate to make dad jokes if you're not actually a father.

It's a faux pa(s).

Russ King thought he had grown up when he got his psychology-based PhD from Cambridge University. Then he became a husband, father and writer. He specialises in making scientific information entertaining and enjoyable to understand. His written work includes the healthcare management textbook *We All Fall Down* and a guide to business networking in the form of a romantic comedy novel *Mixing Business with Pleasure*?

Russ mixes his writing work with being the main carer for his two children aged 13 and 11. He considers it an accomplishment that he made fewer mistakes helping with the second baby than with the first.

Claudia A. Pfeiffer juggles her many roles as a woman, wife, mum of two almost grown up savages, alternative health practitioner, trainer, entrepreneur and writer. With a focus on women's health and the beneficial role of a doula, she accompanies couples before, during and after their  pregnancy. She has helped many men flourish as new fathers when they are given specific roles to fulfill within the new family unit.

She trained with Childbirth Guru Dr. Gowri Motha (Gentle Birth Method) to become a Creative Healing teacher for the German speaking countries. The massage modules presented in this book are part of this gentle and soft technique.

CPSIA information can be obtained
at www.ICGtesting.com
Printed in the USA
BVHW051123010621
608540BV00013B/316

9 783944 411224